The Children's Book of

CHILDREN'S RHYMES

The Children's Book of

CHILDREN'S RHYMES

Compiled by Christopher Logue

Drawings by Bill Tidy

B.T. Batsford Ltd, London

for
Louise King

Hooks and eyes
Joined together
You're a book
And I'm a feather

This compilation © Christopher Logue 1986
First published 1986

ISBN (cased edition) 0 7134 4912 8

Photoset by Servis Filmsetting Ltd, Manchester

Printed in Great Britain by
Butler & Tanner Ltd
Frome, Somerset
for the publisher
B.T. Batsford Ltd
4 Fitzhardinge Street
London W1H 0AH

Contents

To the reader

Silence in the playground
Silence in the street
The biggest fool you ever heard
Is just about to bleat.

It is not easy to say when or where the rhymes in this book were made up, even though some of them mention names and things that can be dated. A few of them are more than a hundred years old. Many of them were circulating when I was eight – in 1933.

They are all common property, and there are almost as many versions of each rhyme as there are rhymers. They are not written and published by adults (like most nursery rhymes) but are concocted by children and passed around by word of mouth. Some are sung to popular tunes, or to tunes of their own, while this or that game is played.

Different versions of about half the rhymes that follow are known all over the English-speaking world – England, Ireland, Scotland, Wales, the United States, Canada, Australia and New Zealand – and some have counterparts in several European languages. I have printed the version I prefer and have avoided punctuation as much as possible. The rhymes were not intended for print but to be said, sung, chanted and yelled, and their beat is as important as their sense.

And that is enough of that.

CHRISTOPHER LOGUE

This book is one thing
My eye is another
Steal not the first
For fear of the other

ONE POTATO

One potato
Two potato
Three potato
Four –
Four potato
Five potato
Six potato
More –
Six potato
Seven potato
Eight potato
Shout ...
Eight potato
Nine potato
Ten potato
Out.

STICKS AND STONES

Sticks and stones
May break my bones
But words will never hurt me
When you're dead
And in your grave
You'll pay for what you called me.

ONE FOR SORROW

One for sorrow
Two for joy
Three for a girl
Four for a boy
Five for silver
Six for gold
Seven a secret that's never been told.

I WENT TO THE
PICTURES NEXT THURSDAY

I went to the pictures next Thursday
I took a front seat at the back
I said to the lady behind me
'I cannot see over your hat.'

She gave me some well-broken biscuits
I ate them and handed them back
I fell through a hole in the ceiling
And broke my breast bone in my back.

WHEN I WAS ONE

When I was one I weighed a ton
When I was two I ate my shoe
When I was three I climbed a tree
When I was four I slammed the door
When I was five I did not thrive
When I was six I laid my bricks
When I was seven I went to Heaven
When I was eight I broke a plate
When I was nine I wrote a line
When I was ten I bought a pen
And here I am – John Abraham!

WEDDING DRESSES

Pink and blue
Will never do

Pink and green
Fit for a queen

Green and white
Out of sight.

UP IN THE MOUNTAINS

Up in the mountains
Lying on the grass
I saw a Frenchman
Sliding on his ★ ★ ★ ★

Ask no questions
Hear no lies
I saw a Frenchman
Doing up his ★ ★ ★ ★ ★

Flies are a nuisance
Flies are a pest
I saw a Frenchman
Doing up his vest.

A SAILOR WENT TO SEA

A sailor went to sea-sea-sea
To see what he could see-see-see
He saw it three times three-three-three
The same as you and me-me-me.
Umpah
Umpah
Stick it up your jumpah
Marmalade and jam –
And all that he could see-see-see
Was the bottom of the deep blue sea-sea-sea
Just like you and me-me-me
Marmalade and jam.

ADAM AND EVE
AND PINCH-ME

Adam and Eve and Pinch-me
Went down to the river to bathe.
Adam and Eve were drowned –
Who do you think was saved?

FOR AN
AUTOGRAPH BOOK

Can't think
Brain numb
Inspiration won't come
Can't write
Bad pen
Best wishes – Amen.

I LIKE SILVER

I like silver
I like brass
I like looking
In the looking-glass.

I like rubies
I like pearls
I like wearing
My hair in curls.

12

HARK THE HERALD
ANGELS SING

Hark! the Herald angels sing
Beecham's Pills are just the thing.

They are gentle meek and mild
Two for a man and one for a child.

If you want to go to Heaven
You must swallow up to seven.

If you want to go to Hell
Take the cardboard box as well.

13

ONE–TWO–THREE

One-two-three-four-five-six-seven
All good children go to Heaven.
Two-three-four-five-six-seven-eight
Other children have to wait.
   Penny on the water
   Tuppence on the sea
   Threepence on the railway
   One-two-three.

KNICKERS AND NAPPIES

What's the time?
Half-past nine
Hang your knickers on the line.

What's the time?
Half past one
Take them off and put them on.

What's the time?
Half-past nine
Hang the nappies on the line.

When they're dry
Bring them in
Don't forget the safety-pin

WHISKERS

Let your whiskers grow
Let your whiskers blow
Why waste money shaving?
Pull 'em out by the roots
And make laces for your boots
Look at the money you're saving.

HOT CROSS BUNS

One-a-penny
Two-a-penny
Hot cross buns.

Three-a-penny
Four-a-penny
Hot cross buns.

If you haven't got a daughter
Give them to your sons.

One-a-penny
Two-a-penny
Hot cross buns.

OPEN THE DOOR

Open the door!
Let me through!
Not without your brown and blue.

Here's my brown!
Here's my blue!
Open the door and let me through!

15

GREAT A

Great A
Little a
Bouncing B
The cat's in the cupboard
And she can't see me.

THE TINKER

Eeny-meeny-miny-mo
Catch a tinker by his toe.

If he hollers let him go
Eeny-meeny-miny-mo.

I SAW ESAU

I saw Esau
Sitting on a seesaw
Esau I saw he.
Esau I saw
Sitting on a seesaw
I saw Esau me.

SECRET MESSAGE

Look beneath the table
Look beneath the lamp
If you want to know my name
Look beneath the stamp.

16

I SCREAM

I scream
You scream
We all scream
'Ice–cream!'

ONE TWO
BUCKLE MY SHOE

One
Two
Buckle my shoe.
Three
Four
Knock at the door.
Five
Six
Pick up sticks.
Seven
Eight
Lay them straight.
Nine
Ten
A big fat hen.
Eleven
Twelve
Dip and delve.
Thirteen
Fourteen
Girls like courting.
Fifteen
Sixteen
In the kitchen.
Seventeen
Eighteen
I am waiting.
Nineteen
Twenty
My stomach's empty.

DID YOU EVER

Did you ever-ever-ever
In your life-life-life
See the devil-devil-devil
Kiss his wife-wife-wife?

SHE DANCED ACROSS
THE BALLROOM FLOOR

She danced across the ballroom floor
Her figure was fantastic
But all of a sudden she rushed to the door –
You can't trust Jones' elastic.

ONE
TWO
THREE

One-two-three
Mother caught a flea
Put it in the teapot
And made a cup of tea.

The flea jumped out
Mother gave a shout
In came father
With his shirt hanging out.

SKIPPING

Two in the middle and two at the end
Each is a sister and each is a friend.
A shilling to save and a penny to spend
Two in the middle and two at the end.

NOT LAST NIGHT
BUT THE NIGHT BEFORE

Not last night but the night before
Two tom cats came knocking at my door.

I went downstairs to let them in
They knocked me down with a rolling pin.

The rolling pin was made of brass
They turned me up and smacked my ★ ★ ★ ★.

ONCE UPON A TIME
WHEN THE BIRDS ATE LIME

Once upon a time when the birds ate lime
And the monkeys chewed tobacco
The pigs took snuff to make them tough
And that's the end of the matter.

ANDY PANDY

Andy Pandy
Sugar candy
Marzipan and rock.
Bread and butter
For your supper
That is all your mother's got

JUMPING JOAN

Here I am
Jumping Joan
Nobody's with me
Always alone.

THE WOODCHUCK

If a woodchuck could chuck
All the wood
That a woodchuck would
How much wood
Could a woodchuck chuck
If a woodchuck would chuck wood?

LADIES AND GENTLEMEN

Ladies and Gentlemen, I come before you
to stand behind you to tell you something
I know nothing about. On last Thursday
there will be a mother's meeting
for fathers only.
    Admission is free
    Pay at the door
    Bring your own chairs
    And sit on the floor.

THE SPANISH LADY

Walking through the city
At half past eight at night
I saw a Spanish lady
Washing her clothes by night.

First she rubbed them
Then she scrubbed them
Then she hung them up to dry
Then she laid her hands upon them
Saying 'I wish my clothes were dry'.

THE THREE CHILDREN

Three little children on the sand
Along comes an old woman and takes them in hand

She took them to a secret part
And stuck her penknife in their heart.

VALENTINES

A song is a song
A dance is a dance
What is life
Without romance?

★

Sugar is sugar
Tea is tea
I love you
Do you love me?

★

A gun's a gun
A trigger's a trigger
What's a girl
Without a figure?

Butter is butter
Cheese is cheese
What's a kiss
Without a squeeze?

★

Knee to knee
Hip to hip
Cheek to cheek
Lip to lip.

★

Bread is bread
Ham is ham
You'll need the strength
I'll push the pram.

BOY	GIRL
Boy	Girl
Garden	Gate
Standing	Kissing
Very	Late
Dad	Comes
Big	Boots
Boy	Runs
Girl	Scoots

TELL YOUR MUM
TO HOLD HER TONGUE

Tell your mum to hold her tongue
She loved a boy when she was young.

Tell your dad to do the same
He was the one who changed her name.

CABBAGE

My love is like a cabbage
Divided into two.

The leaves I leave to others
The heart I give to you.

PANTS

I see London
I see France
I see Laura's underpants.

Neither black
Neither white –
Oh my God they're dynamite!

APOLOGY

Please forgive my being bold
I should have written your name in gold.
But gold is scarce and ink must do
Just to tell you – I love you.

CAUTION

Never kiss your lover at the garden gate
Love is blind, but the neighbours ain't.

JINGLE JANGLE

Jingle jangle
Silver bangle
You look cute
From every angle.

APPLES ARE RED

Apples are red
My nose is blue
Standing at the bus stop
Waiting for you.

A RED HEART

A red heart means I love you
A blue heart means I care
A black heart means I hate you
And that's why I'm not there.

A NOTE

If for me there is no hope
Send me back a yard of rope.

I AM RUBBER

I am rubber
You are glue
All the nasty things you say
Rub off me
And stick to you.

THERE I WAS

There I was
Broken-hearted –
Tried to cry
But only farted.
Ha! Ha! Ha!

27

I SAID MY PYJAMAS

I said my pyjamas
I put on my prayers
I went up my slippers
I took off my stairs
I switched off the bed
I jumped in the light
The reason for this is
You kissed me goodnight.

L STANDS FOR LONDON

L stand for London
T stands for Town
H stands for Harry
B stands for Brown.

Harry Brown of London Town
Said he'd marry me.
Isn't it a blessing
To sit on Harry's knee?

Monday is my washing day
Tuesday I am done
Wednesday is my ironing day
Thursday I am done.

Friday is my shopping day
Saturday I'm done
Sunday is my letter day –
Will Harry never come?

CHERRIES ARE RED

Cherries are red
Nuts are brown
Petticoats up
Trousers down.

SHE OFFERED
HER HONOUR

She offered her honour
She honoured her offer
And all through the night
He was on her and off her.

KISSES

Some kiss under the mistletoe
Some underneath the rose
But the place I'd like to kiss you
Is underneath your nose.

★

Kisses spread germs
So it's stated.
Kiss me baby
I'm vaccinated.

★

2 in the car
2 wee kisses
2 weeks later
Mr and Mrs.

★

Remember the night
We met in the hall?
You missed my lips
And kissed the wall.

★

Two in a hammock
Going to kiss
All of a sudden
They ended up like SIH.L

★

I'm in love
And love is bliss
How many times
Do I get a kiss?

I LOVE YOU

I love you
I love you
I love you almighty
I wish your pyjamas
Were next to my nightie.

Don't be mistaken
Don't be misled
I mean on the clothes line
And not in the bed.

ALL THE GIRLS
IN OUR TOWN

All the girls in our town
Live a happy life
Except for Sandra Wilson
Who wants to be a wife.

A wife she would be
According to the law –
So up came Jimmy
And knocked upon her door.

She kissed him and cuddled him
And sat him on her knee
And said 'Little Jimmy
Will you marry me?'

'With a new-swept carpet
A new-made bed
A new cup and saucer
We will be wed.'

Yes–no–yes–no–yes–no–yes.

DOWN IN THE VALLEY

Down in the valley
Where the green grass grows
Mary Gray
Looking like a rose.

Mary Gray
Tall and sweet
Calls her lover
At the end of the street.

'Sweetheart, sweetheart
Will you marry me?'
'Yes, dear Mary
At half-past three.'

Ice cake and currant cake
All for tea —
We will have a wedding
At half-past three.

WIND BLOWS LOW,
WIND BLOWS HIGH

Wind blows low, wind blows high
Rain comes falling from the sky
Mary Thompson thinks she'll die
For want of the Golden City.

She is handsome, she is pretty
She is the girl of the Golden City.

All the boys are fighting for her.
All the girls think nothing of her.

Let the boys say what they will
Jamie Jack has got her still.

Now he takes her by the hand
Now he leads her over the water
Gives her kisses one-two-three
Mrs Thompson's handsome daughter.

Wind blows low, wind blows high
Rain comes falling from the sky
Mary Thompson thinks she'll die
For want of the Golden City.

MARRIAGE

Needles
Pins
Triplets
Twins
When a girl marries
Her trouble begins.

★

Now you are married you must obey
And must be true in all you say.
You must be kind, you must be good
And help your wife to chop the wood.

★

I should worry
I should care
I should marry a millionaire.
Should he die
I should cry
Then I should marry another guy.

★

Who is coming down the street?
Betty Martin, ain't she sweet.
She's been married twice before.
Now she's knocking on Joe's door.

News is come to town
Polly Dawson's married.

You can tell the parson's wife
You can tell the beadle
You can iron her wedding dress
I will thread her needle.

What will you give to show your hope?
A candlestick that's broken.
A chip of soap, and a twist of rope.
Out you go
Out you go
For a dirty miser.
If you live to ninety
I hope you will be wiser.

                ★

When we get married
We will have quads
Two will be punks
Two will be mods.

                ★

Here comes the bride
Short, fat and wide
Had to take the doors off
To get her inside.

Here comes the groom
Thin as a broom –
Holding his breath in
To give her more room.
            [or]
Here comes the groom.
No more room.

ONCE A KING

Once a king – always a king
Once a knight – that's all right.

NAPPIES

Electricated nappies
They take a hundred batt'ries.
You turn them on –
BANG! BANG! BANG!
Your baby's gone.

THIS IS THE DAY

This is the day
They give babies away
With half a pound of tea.

Open the lid
And find your kid
With a ten-year guarantee.

SMUDGE SMUDGE

Smudge smudge
Tell the judge
Mum's got a new baby.

Not a girl
Not a boy
Just a new-born baby.

Wrap it up in tissue paper
Take it to the elevator.
    First floor – wink.
    Next floor – pout.
    Third floor – squeak,
    Then throw the baby out.

OVER THE GARDEN WALL

Over the garden wall
I let the baby fall
Me Ma came out
And gave me a clout
Over the garden wall.

ON THE PO

Eenie-meni-miny-mo
Put the baby on the po.
When its done
Wipe its bum
With a piece of chewing gum.

COPPER COPPER

'Copper, copper, don't touch me
I have a wife and family.'
'How many children have you got?'
'Five-and-twenty is my lot.'

MY MUM

My mum
Your mum
Lived across the way.

Sixteen
Seventeen
Old Cowsway.

Each night
They'd fight
This is what they'd say:

'Up and down the parlour
In and out the square
Girls are made of cotton
Boys are made of hair.'

MUMMY

Mummy
Daddy
Uncle Joe
Went to London in a po.
The po burst
Daddy cursed
Mummy went to Heaven first.

MY OLD MAN

My old man's a dustman
He wears a dustman's hat
He bought a season ticket
To see a football match.

The kick-off was from Fatty
And then the whistle blew
So Knocker lost his temper
And down the field he flew.

Fatty passed to Knocker
Knocker passed it back
Fatty took a header
And laid poor Knocker flat.

They put him on a stretcher
And carried him to bed
They rubbed his belly with a lump of jelly
And this is what he said:
   'Happy Birthday to you
   Mashed potato and stew
   That's the end of my story
   Happy Birthday to you.'

MOTHER

Mother, may I go out to swim?
Yes, my darling daughter –
Hang your clothes on the gooseberry bush
And don't go near the water.

THE MILKING PAIL

Mother buy me a milking pail.
  One-two-three.
Where's the money coming from?
  One-two-three.
Sell your husband's feather bed.
  One-two-three.
What will my husband go to sleep in?
  One-two-three.
Your husband can sleep in the pigsty.
  One-two-three.
Where will the pig go to sleep in?
  One-two-three.
The pig can sleep in the washing-tub.
  One-two-three.
What will I do my washing in?
  One-two-three.
Do your washing in a thimble.
  One-two-three.
What will I sew your Sunday clothes with?
  One-two-three.
Sew your Sunday clothes with a poker.
  One-two-three.
What will I poke the fire with?
  One-two-three.
Poke the fire with your finger.
  One-two-three.
What will happen if I burn my finger?
  One-two-three.
  Suck it and see!
  Suck it and see!
  One-two-three.

PENALTIES

Step on a crack
And break your father's back.
Step on a line
And break your mother's spine.
Step on a ditch
Your sister's nose will itch.
Step into dirt
And tear your brother's shirt.

COLD MEAT

Cold meat
Mutton chops
Tell me when your mother drops.
I will come and pick her up
Cold meat
Mutton chops.

HAVE YOU
GOT A SISTER

Have you got a sister?
    I have kissed her.
Have you got a brother?
    Made of india rubber.
Have you got a baby?
    Made of bread and gravy.

UNCLE JACK

You know my Uncle Jack?
He had a wooden back.
Every time you knocked him down
You got your money back.

AUNTIE JEAN

Long live our Auntie Jean
She lives in Aberdeen
Long may she sell ice-cream.
Long live Aunt Jean
Give us a double a cone
Make it weigh half a stone
Then we will always groan
Long live Aunt Jean.

MY AUNT JANE

My aunt Jane
She called me in
Gave me tea out of her wee tin.
Half a bap
Sugar on the top
Three black lumps out of her wee shop.

UNCLE HENRY

Uncle Henry
Went to work
In his Mini-Minor
Crashed into an atom bomb
And finished up in China.

GRANNY

You mustn't shove your granny off a bus
You mustn't shove your granny off a bus
You mustn't shove your granny
For she's your mammy's mammy
You mustn't shove your granny off a bus.

AUNTIE MARY

Auntie Mary
Had a canary
Up the leg of her drawers.
It whistled for hours
And frightened the Boers
And won the Victoria Cross.

BILLY

My brother Billy
Had a three-foot willy
And he showed it to the girl next door.
She thought it was a snake
So she hit it with a rake
And now it's only two-foot-four.

FATTY

Tatty Fatty
Five by four
Can't get through the bathroom door.

JANE

Jane is mad
I am glad
I know how to please her
A pint of gin
To make her grin
And you and me to squeeze her.

TINY TIM

I had a little brother
His name was Tiny Tim
I put him in the bathtub
To teach him how to swim.

He drank all the water
He ate all the soap
And he died last night
With a bubble in his throat.

Send for the doctor
Send for the nurse
Send for the lady
With the alligator purse.

'Dead,' said the doctor
'Dead,' said the nurse
'Dead,' said the lady
With the alligator purse.

SUE

I charge my daughters everyone
To keep good house while I am gone.
You and you, but mostly Sue –
Or I'll beat you black and blue.

TILLY THE TOILER

Tilly the Toiler
Never late
Always in school
By half-past eight.

SEE, SEE,
MY BONNY

See, see, my bonny
I cannot play with you
My little sister's got the mumps
My big one's got the flu.

Slide down the drainpipe
I'll shut the door
See you round the corner
At quarter past four.

I'M NOT — SAYS SHE

I'm not — says she
So smart — says she
Nor yet — says she
As big — says she
But I'll go — says she
To Perth — says she
And get — says she
A man — says she
And then — says she
I'll be — says she
As good — says she
As you — says she.

VICTIM OF THE
CHINESE BURN

I LOVE ME

I love me
I think I'm grand
I go to the films
And hold my hand.

I put my hand
Around my waist
And if it roams
I slap my face.

OH MY FINGER

Oh my finger
Oh my thumb
Oh my belly
Oh my bum.

I WENT TO A
CHINESE LAUNDRY

I went to a Chinese Laundry
I went for a piece of bread
They wrapped me up in a tablecloth
And sent me off to bed.

I saw an Indian maiden.
She stood about ten feet high
Her hair was painted sky-blue pink
And she only had one eye.

I saw a pillar box floating
I jumped in rather cool
It only took me fourteen days
To get to Liverpool.

I SAY I LOVE YOU

I say I love you
I say I love you
I say I love you
Is it true?

If you will love me
If you will love me
If you will love me
I'll love you.

I MUST

I must I must
Increase my bust!

I will I will
Get bigger still!

Hurrah hurrah
A bigger bra!

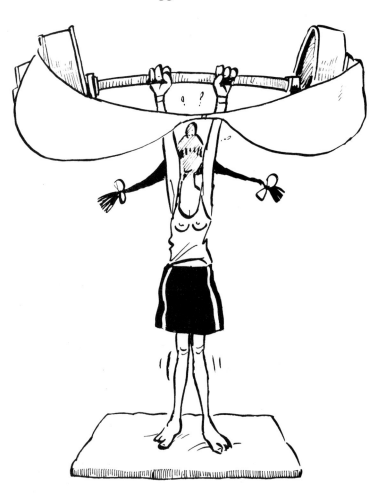

I PASSED BY
YOUR WINDOW

I passed by your window
I saw you undress
I saw your blue pyjamas
I saw your white vest.

I would have seen more
But fate was unkind
Just at that moment
You pulled down the blind.

SHOCKING

Shocking!
Shocking!
Shocking!
A mouse ran up my stocking.
What did it see
When it got to my knee?
Shocking!
Shocking!
Shocking!

I HAD A BLOKE
IN WAPPING

I had a bloke in Wapping
I had a bloke in Kent
I had a bloke in Brighton
And this is what he sent:
    Marmalade and treacle
    Ginger-beer and jam
    Some for me, some for you
    Some for Uncle Sam.

I HAD A DOLLY

I had a dolly
Dressed in green
I didn't like her
I gave her to the Queen.

The Queen didn't like her
She gave her to her cat
The cat didn't like her
Because she wasn't fat.

GETTING ON

Now I know my alpahabet
I can get my knickers wet.

51

DUNCE

Dunce
Dunce
Double D
Cannot learn his ABC.
In the corner you will see
Dunce
Dunce
Double D.

CAN YOU READ

Can you read?
Can you write?
Can you smoke your mother's pipe?

MISS

Please Miss, my mother, Miss,
I've come to tell you this, Miss,
I, Miss, won't, Miss,
Be at school tomorrow, Miss.

TEACHER

Teacher
Teacher
Do your duty
Here comes Joan
The raving beauty.
She does high-kicks
She does splits
She knows all the latest hits.

FIRECRACKER

Firecracker
Firecracker
Boom!
Boom!
Boom!
Firecracker
Firecracker
Boom!
Boom!
Boom!
Boys have got the muscles
Teacher's got the brains
Girls have got the sexy legs
We've won the game.

APRIL FOOL

April Fool
Go to school
Tell the teacher
She's a mule.
If she slaps you
Do not cry –
Take your books and say 'Goodbye!'

GOD MADE BEES

God made bees
Bees make honey
We do the work
But teachers get the money.

SCHOOL DINNERS

Scab and matter custard
Snot and bogy pie
Dead dog's giblets
And squashed cat's eye.
Spread it on your Hovis
Spread it good and thick
Wash it all down
With a cup of cold sick.

*

If you eat school dinners
Better watch your hide
A lot of kids didn't
And a lot of kids died.
The meat is iron
And the spuds are steel
If they don't get you
Then the afters will.

STINKER

Poor old Stinker's dead and gone
We'll see his face no more
For what he thought was H_2O
Was H_2SO_4.

LATIN

Latin is a dead tongue
Dead as dead can be
First it killed the Romans
Now it's killing me.

They are dead who spoke it
They are dead who wrote it
They are dead who learnt it
Lucky them, they earnt it.

NATURAL DISASTER

If your school is flooded
Do not fear to die.
Climb upon your Latin book
For that is always dry.

BREAKING UP

This time next week I shall be
Out of this academy.

No more Latin, no more French
No more sitting on a hard school bench.

No more stale bread and butter
No more water from the gutter.

No more maggots in the spam
No more gobs of damson jam.

No more beatles in my tea
Making googly eyes at me.

If the master interferes
Knock him down and box his ears.

If he's not content with that
Fry his face in bacon fat.

If that does not serve him right
Blow him up with dynamite.

THE MULE

My mother was a wall-eyed goat
My father was an ass
I feed myself off leather
And bottle tops and grass.
I'm a mule, a mule
A long-eared fool
Never had a lesson
For I never went to school.

WHAT'S YOUR NAME

What's your name?
Mary Jane.
Where do you live?
Cabbage Lane.
What's your number?
Rain and thunder.
What address?
Watercress.

CHARLIE MCGRORY

I'll tell you a story
Of Charlie McGrory.
A hole in the wall
And that is all.

DICKY DICKY DOUT

Dicky Dicky Dout
With his shirt hanging out
Four yards in
And four yards out.

POLLY

Polly had a dolly
That was sick-sick-sick
So she telephoned the doctor
To come quick-quick-quick.

Round came the doctor
With his bag and hat
And he rapped on the door
With a rat-ta-tat-tat.

He looked at Polly's dolly
And this is what he said
'Polly put your dolly
Into bed-bed-bed.'

'Here is the paper
For a pill-pill-pill
And I'll see you tomorrow
With my bill-bill-bill.'

SANDY CANDY

Sandy Candy
Blows his horn
Miles and miles
Among the corn.

SUSAN BLUE

Susan Blue
How do you do?
Please may I go for a walk with you?
Where to?
I know —
In the field where the daisies grow.

SUZIE

When Suzie was a baby, a baby Suzie was.
She went 'Goo-goo-goo.'
She went 'Ga-ga-ga.'

When Suzie was a school-girl, a school-girl Suzie was.
She said 'Miss-Miss-Miss
Tell me where the toilet is.'

When Suzie was a teener, a teener Suzie was.
She went 'Ah-oo-ah! I lost my bra.
I left it in my boy-friend's car.'

When Suzie was a mother, a mother Suzie was.
She said 'Rock-rock-rock
Got a hole in your sock.'

When Suzie was a grandma, a grandma Suzie was.
She went 'Knit-knit-knit
Oh I lost that stitch-stitch-stitch.'

MABEL

Mabel, Mabel
Strong and able
Get your elbows off the table.

MARY MACK

Mary Mack
Dressed in black
Three gold buttons down her back.

I love coffee
I love tea
I love the boys and the boys love me.

I asked my mother
For fifty pence
To see the elephant jump the fence.

He jumped so high
He touched the sky
And never came back till the end of July.

One flew east
One flew west
One flew over the cuckoo's nest.

THE DUTCH GIRL

I am a pretty little Dutch girl
As pretty as pretty can be
And all the boys in the baseball team
Go crazy over me.

My mother sent me shopping
And told me not to stay.
I met a member of the team
And stayed till Christmas day.

CAROLINE

Ipsy tipsy Caroline
Washed her hair in turpentine
Thinks that it will make her shine
Ipsy tipsy Caroline.

WILLIAM ARLIE

William Arlie
Stole some barley
Out of a baker's shop.
The baker came out
And gave him a clout
And made poor William hop.

LITTLE NELLIE

Little Nellie in her tent
Can't afford to pay the rent
Mr Landlord gave a shout
'Put her out, put her out.'
   Not because she's dirty
   Not because she's clean
   All because she's had measles and mumps
   With chicken-pox in-between.

ALGY

Algy met a bear
The bear met Algy
The bear grew bulgy
The bulge was Algy.

DANCING DOLLY

Dancing Dolly had no sense
Bought a fiddle for fifty pence.
All the music she could play
Was 'Over the hills and far away'.

JOHNNY CHEEVER

Johnny Cheever is no good
Chop him up for firewood.
When he's dead, bake his head
Turn it into gingerbread.

SALLY

Sally go round the moon
Sally go round the sun
Sally go round the omnilebus
On a Sunday afternoon.

JOHN

John and a chimpanzee
Sitting on a rail.
What is the difference?
John has no tail.

ABDUL

Abdul bought a motor car
And swapped it for a camel
He didn't like the colour
So he sprayed it with enamel.
The enamel stayed all sticky
While crossing the Sahara
And when he tried to get it off
It stuck to his tarara.

CHARLIE

Charlie over the water
Charlie over the sea
Charlie catch a blackbird
But can't catch me.

Charlie likes whiskey
Charlie likes brandy
Charlie likes kissing girls
O sugar candy!

MARY ROSE

Mary Rose
Sat on a pin.
Mary Rose ...

64

ACKER BACKER

Acker Backer
Soda cracker
Acker Backer four
Acker Backer
Soda cracker
Knock on Acker's door.

MOLLY MACK

'Molly Mack, my shirt is black
What shall I wear on Sunday?'
'Go to bed and cover your head
And not get up till Monday.'

LOUIE LOUIE

Louie Louie
Fooey fooey
I think you are full of hooey.

JEAN

Jean-Jean-Jean
The cat is at the cream
Supping with her forefeet
And glowering with her een.

TOM JILL AND BOB

Tom tied a tin to the tail of a cat
Jill put a brick in a blind man's hat
Bob threw his grandma down the stairs
They all died young and nobody cares.

JANE AND LOUISA

Jane and Louisa will soon come home
   Soon come home
   Soon come home
Jane and Louisa will soon come home
Into this beautiful garden.

My dear will you have me pick a rose
   Pick a rose
   Pick a rose
My dear will you have me pick a rose
In this beautiful garden?

My dear will you let me waltz with you
   Waltz with you
   Waltz with you
My dear will you let me waltz with you
In this beautiful garden?

OLD PEGGY

Poor old Peggy's dead
She died last night in bed
We put her in a coffin
And she fell right through the bottom
Poor old Peggy's dead.

OLD RODGER

Old Rodger is dead and gone to his grave
   He-hi – gone to his grave.
They planted an apple-tree over his head
   He-hi – over his head.
The apples grew ripe and ready to drop
   He-hi – ready to drop.
There came an old woman from Hippety-Hop
   He-hi – Hippety-Hop.
She began picking them picking them up
   He-hi – picking them up.
Old Rodger got up and gave her a knock
   He-hi – gave her a knock.
Which made the old woman from Hippety-Hop
   He-hi – go Hippety-Hop.

OLD MEG

Old Meg was a gypsy
She lived on the moors
Her bed was the heather
Her home out of doors.

No breakfast at morn
No dinner at noon
And for her supper
She stared at the moon.

SAM

Sam
Sam
The dirty old man
Washed his face in a frying pan
Combed his hair with the leg of a chair
Sam
Sam
The dirty old man.

COLOURED LADIES

Mrs White
Had a fright
In the middle of the night.
Saw a ghost
Eating toast
Half-way up a lamp-post.

★

Mrs Brown
Went to town
With her knickers hanging down.

★

Mrs Green
Saw the Queen
On the television screen.

★

Mrs Pink
Washed her mink
In a bucket by the sink.

★

Mrs Red
Went to bed
In the morning she was dead.

MR MUNDAY

'Mr Munday how's your wife?'
'Very sick and like to die.'
'Can she eat butcher meat?'
'More than I can buy.
Half a horse, half a cow.
Half three-quarters of a sow.'
'Make her porridge extra thin.
Put half a pound of butter in.'

MRS SMITH

I went around
I dropped a pin
I asked if Mrs Smith was in.
'She is not without
She is not within
She is up in the attic
Drinking gin.'
Down she came
As white as milk
With a rose on her breast
As soft as silk.

FIRE

'Fire! Fire!' says Obadiah.
'Where? Where?' says Mrs Pear.
'Behind the rocks,' says Doctor Fox.
'Put it out!' says Mr Trout.
'I've no bucket,' said Lord MacTucket.
'Use my shoe,' said I.O.U.

OLD MOTHER ROUNDABOUT

Old Mother Roundabout
Knocking all the kids about
Outside Elsie's door.
Up comes Elsie with a stick
And lets her know what for.

MR PADBURY

Old Padbury's got a bunion
A face like a pickled onion
A nose like a squashed tomato
And legs like two sticks.

MR KELLY

Old Mister Kelly
Had a pimple on his belly
His wife cut it off
And it tasted like jelly.

PANCAKES

Mix the pancake
Stir the pancake
Pop it in the pan,
Fry the pancake
Toss the pancake
Catch it if you can.

EAPER WEAPER

Eaper Weaper
Chimney-sweeper
Had a wife but
Couldn't keep her.

Had another
Didn't love her
Up the chimney
Eaper shoved her.

THE WIDOW OF BABYLON

Here's a poor widow from Babylon
Six poor children and all alone.
One can cook, one can brew,
One can cut, one can sew.
One can sit by the fire and spin
And one can bake a cake for a king.
  Some choose east
  Some choose west
  Some choose the one that they love best.

WHO ARE YOU?

Who are you?
A dirty old man
Always been since I began
My ma and my pa
Were dirty before me
Never had a wash since 1940.

WORMS

Nobody loves me
Everybody hates me
Going in the garden
To eat worms.
Big fat juicy ones
Little squiggly iggly ones
Going in the garden
To eat worms.

MORE RAIN

It's raining
It's pouring
The old man is snoring.

He went to bed
He bumped his head
And couldn't get up in the morning.

DISASTER

The night was dark and stormy
The toilet light was dim
We heard him shout for all his worth
'My God – I've fallen in!'

MANNERS

If you sprinkle
When you winkle
Please be neat
And wipe the seat.

THREE OLD LADIES

Oh, dear, what can the matter be?
Three old ladies locked in the lavatory
They were there from Monday to Saturday
Nobody knew they were there.

SILLY OLD MAN

Silly old man
Silly old man
Walks alone
With an old tin can.

His old tin can
His old tin can
Is full of worms
He eats them!
He eats them!

Can't get a wife
Can't get a wife
Silly old man
He eats them!

74

FIVE OLD FISHERMEN

Five old fishermen
Sitting on a bridge
One caught a tiddler
One caught a fridge.

One caught a tadpole
One caught an eel
And the fifth one caught
A perambulator wheel.

LEMONADE

Lemonade
Made in the shade
Stirred with a spade
By an old maid.

HINX MINX

Hinx minx
The old witch stinks
The fat begins to fry,
Nobody home
But Jumping Joan
Jumping Joan and I.

CHESTY

It was a cough
That carried him off.
It was a coffin
They carried him off in.

THE BOY STOOD ON
THE BURNING DECK

The boy stood on the burning deck
His feet were full of blisters
The flames came up and burned his pants
And now he wears his sister's.

BOGIES

We have joy
We have fun
Flicking bogies at the sun.
When the sun
Gets high and hot
All the bogies
Turn to snot.

THIS OLD MAN

This old man
He played one
He played nicknack on my bum.
Nicknack paddywhack
Give a dog a bone
This old man came rolling home.

This old man
He played two
He played nicknack on my shoe.
Nicknack paddywhack
Give a dog a bone
This old man came rolling home.

This old man
He played three
He played nicknack on my knee
Nicknack paddywhack
Give a dog a bone
This old man came rolling home.

This old man
He played four
He played nicknack on my door.
Nicknack paddywhack
Give a dog a bone
This old man came rolling home.

This old man
He played five
He played nicknack on my hide.
Nicknack paddywhack
Give a dog a bone
This old man came rolling home.

This old man
He played six
He played nicknack on my knicks.
Nicknack paddywhack
Give a dog a bone
This old man came rolling home.

This old man
He played seven
He played nicknack up to Heaven.
Nicknack paddywhack
Give a dog a bone
This old man came rolling home.

This old man
He played eight
He played nicknack on my plate.
Nicknack paddywhack
Give a dog a bone
This old man came rolling home.

This old man
He played nine
He played nicknack on my spine.
Nicknack paddywhack
Give a dog a bone
This old man came rolling home.

This old man
He played ten
He played nicknack on my pen.
Nicknack paddywhack
Give a dog a bone
This old man came rolling home.

AFTER THE BALL

After the ball was over
After the last goodbye
She put her false teeth in water
And took out her best glass eye.
She put her false leg in the cupboard
And hung up her wig on the wall
And the rest of her went to bye-byes
After the ball.

ROSES AND VIOLETS

Roses are red
Violets are blue
Lemons are sour
And so are you.

★

Roses are red
Violets are blue
Carnations smell sweet
And so do you.

★

Roses are red
Violets are black
You'd look good
With a knife in your back.

★

Roses are red
Violets are green
You need to go
In a washing-machine.

★

Roses are red
Violets are bluish
If it wasn't for Jesus
We'd all be Jewish.

★

Roses are red
Violets are blue
Rain on the window
Reminds me of you –
    Drip! Drip!

THE POST

De liver
De letter
De sooner
De better.

★

Postman
Postman
Do your duty
Take this to my bathing beauty.

Postman
Postman
Don't delay
Do the quickstep on your way.

Postman
Postman
If she's gone
Leave it with her brother John.

★

Early in the morning
Half-past eight
Hear the postman at the gate.
Postman
Postman
Take a cup.
Lady, pick your letter up.
Echo
Echo
White and flat
See a letter on the mat.
Early in the morning
Eight o'clock
You will hear the postman knock.

GREEN GRAVEL

Green gravel
Green gravel
Your grass is so green
I'll send you a letter
To call Florrie in.
I'll wash you in milk
And dress you in silk
And write your name
With a gold cane.

COBBLER

Cobbler
Cobbler
Mend my shoe.
Have it done by half-past two.
Half-past two
Is much too late
Have it done by half-past eight.

THE BARBER

Tiddly Wink the barber
Went to shave his father
Soap slip
Cut lip
Tiddly Wink the barber.

THE BLACKSMITH

Light the fire, blacksmith
Show a pretty light
In comes Lucy
Dressed in white.

Pretty shoes and stockings
Pretty curly hair
Pretty beads around her neck
But no chemise to wear.

HELLO SIR

'Hello, sir.'
'Hello, sir.'
'Come to see the grocer?'
'No, sir.'
'Why, sir?'
'Because I have a cold, sir.'
'Where'd you get the cold, sir?'
'Up at the North Pole, sir.'
'Why were you there, sir?'
'Shooting polar bears, sir.'
'How many did you kill, sir?'
'Enough to pay my bill, sir.'

GIRL GUIDE

I'm a little Girl Guide dressed in blue
And these are the actions I must do:
Salute the captain
Curtsey to the Queen
Show my knickers to the football team.

WALLFLOWERS

Water
Water
Wallflower
Growing up high
We are all children
And we must die.
Except for Nellie Newton
The youngest of all
She can dance
She can sing
She can laugh at everything.
  Fie, for shame!
  Fie, for shame!
  Turn your face to the wall again.

PIPS

The First Lieutenant who was so neat
Stopped in the battle to wash his feet.

HERE COMES THE VICAR

Here comes the Vicar riding
   Riding, riding
Here comes the Vicar riding
   Up to my door.

What are you riding up for?
   Up for, up for
What are you riding up for?
   Up to my door.

He's riding here to marry
   To marry, to marry
He's riding here to marry
   To marry everyone.

'Do you want to marry
   To marry, to marry
Do you want to marry?'
   No, Vicar! No!

THE PREACHER

The Preacher in his pulpit
Could not say his prayers
He giggled and he gaggled
Till he fell downstairs.
The stairs gave a crack
He broke his humpty back
And all the congregation
Gave a quack-quack-quack.

PARSON DARBY

Parson Darby wore a black gown
And every button cost half-a-crown.
From port to port, from toe to toe
Turn the ship and away we go.

DOCTOR DOCTOR

Doctor
Doctor
Can you tell
What will make a sick man well?

Take a bowl full of lice
When the lice begin to crawl
Take a spoon and eat them all.

★

Doctor
Doctor
Will I die?
Yes, my child
And so will I.

TRUTH

Truth
Truth
Nobody's daughter
Took off her clothes and jumped in the water.

HOSIE

Hosie
Hosie
Peep-peep-peep
Where is the man with cloven feet?
Where's his house and where's his street?
Hosie
Hosie
Peep-peep-peep.

LIAR

Liar
Liar
Lipstick
Born on a broomstick.
God send fire
To burn a little liar.

TELL YOU THE TRUTH

Tell you the truth
And I'm not lying
I have to walk backwards
To keep from flying.

HOURS ASLEEP

Nature needs six
Custom gives seven
Lazy takes nine
And wicked eleven.

FRIENDS

Make friends
Make friends
Never never break friends.
If you do
Catch the flu
That will be the end of you.

CARELESS

Don't care was made to care
Don't care was hung
Don't care was put in a pot
And boiled till he was done.

I DECLARE

I declare it a rule
That a man is a fool
To want hot when it's cool
To want cool when it's hot
Always wanting to be what he's not.
I declare it a rule
Such a man is a fool.

SEEING AN AMBULANCE

Touch your collar
Never swallow
Never get the fever.
Not for you
Not for me
Not for all the family.
Touch my nose
Touch my toes
Never go in one of those.

2 Y'S

2 y's u r
2 y's u b
I c u r
2 y's 4 me.

CROSS MY HEART

Cross my heart
Hope to die
Stick a needle
In my eye.

BAD GIVER

Give a thing
Take it back
God will ask you
'What is that?'

If you say
You don't know
God will send you
Down below.

ASHES AND DUST

Ashes to ashes
Dust to dust
Give me a kiss
Before I rust.

★

Ashes to ashes
Dust to dust
If God won't have you
The Devil must.

★

Ashes to ashes
Dust to dust
If you don't like my waistline
Hands off my bust.

BEER IS BEER

Beer is beer
Honey is honey
It takes two rabbits
To make a bunny.

FINDERS AND LOSERS

Finders keepers
Losers weepers.

MUSICAL
DIRECTIONS

Never B♭
Sometimes B#
Always B♯

RIDDLES

Sisters and brothers
Have I none
But this man's father
Is my father's son.
Who?

★

Little Miss Ettigoat
In a white petticoat
With a gold nose –
The longer she stands
The shorter she grows.
A lighted candle

★

What is it that
Goes over your head
And under your hat?
Hair

★

East–west–north–south
Hundreds of teeth
No mouth.
A saw

PINS

See a pin
Pick it up
All day long
Have good luck.
See a pin
Pass it by
Need a pin
Before you die.

SNEEZING

Once – a wish
Twice – a letter
Three times – a kiss
Four times – something better.

STAR LIGHT
STAR BRIGHT

Star light
Star bright
You're the first I see tonight.
I wish I may
I wish I might
I wish my very wish tonight.

WISHING

Pinkety-pankety
Thumb to thumb
Make a wish
It's sure to come.

When yours comes true
Mine will too
Pinkety-pankety
Thumb to thumb.

STAG–A–RAG

Stag-a-rag-a-roaming
Very frosty bright
What I do not catch today
I'll catch tomorrow night.

MOON

I see the moon
And the moon sees me.
God bless the moon
And God bless me.

RAIN

Rain
Rain
Go away.
Come again another day.

IN THE GARDEN

Went to the garden
Picked up a pin
Asked who was out
Asked who was in.
Nobody in
Nobody out
Down in the garden
Walking about.

THE LAND OF MARS

In the land of Mars
The ladies smoke cigars
And every puff they take
Is enough to kill a snake.
When the snake is dead
They put roses on its head.

UP AND DOWN

Up and down
Up and down
All the way to London Town.
Swish swash
Swish swash
All the way to Charing Cross.
Heel and toe
Heel and toe
All the way to Jericho.

BANGOR BOAT'S AWAY

Bangor boat's away!
We have no time to stay
One in a boat
Two in a boat
Bangor boat's away!

BUM BUM BAILEY-O

Bum Bum bailey-o
Two to one a nailey-o
Barbel-ee barbel-o
Bum bum bailey-o.

PROVERB

Never let your braces dangle
While you're standing near the mangle.

THREE KINGS

We three kings of Orient are
One in a taxi
One in a car
One on a scooter
Blowing his hooter
Smoking a big cigar.

★

We three kings of Leicester Square
Selling ladies' underwear.
No elastic!
How fantastic!
Only 50p a pair!

THE QUEEN
MAKES HER CURTSEY

The Queen makes her curtsey
The King makes his bow
The boys go kiss-kiss-kiss
The girls go – Wow!

95

PLEASE KEEP
OFF THE GRASS

Please keep off the grass, sir
And let the ladies pass, sir.
You know the rule
You silly fool –
Please keep off the grass, sir.

INKY PINKY LANE

As I was walking down the Inky Pinky Lane
I met some Inky Pinky children.
They asked me this
They asked me that
They asked me the colour of the Union Jack.
'Red white and blue, which colour suits you?'
'Red!'
'Red is for danger, danger, danger.
Red is for danger, so out go you.'
'White!'
'White is for wedding, wedding, wedding.
White is for wedding, so out go you.'
'Blue!'
'Blue is for angel, angel, angel.
Blue is for angel, so out go you.'

LOOK ON
THE MANTELPIECE

Look on the mantelpiece
You will find a ball of grease
Shining like a threepenny-piece.
High-ho, Silver.

COLOURS

Blue-blue catch the flu
Who will want to play with you.

Red-red wet his bed
Wipe it up with gingerbread.

Green-green like a queen
Stick her head in gasoline.

Yellow-yellow kissed a fellow
Go to bed and eat some Jell-O.

Black-black sit on a tack
You will break your mother's back.

White-white looks a fright
Thinks she will get squeezed tonight.

WOULD YOU LEND
MY MOTHER A SAUCEPAN?

Would you lend my mother a saucepan?
Would you lend my mother a spoon?
Because she's going to have
Some friends to tea this afternoon.

Would you lend my mother half-a-crown
This morning, Mrs Burke?
She'll pay you back on Wednesday
When my father gets some work.

97

RHUBARB

Shine your windows with rhubarb
It only costs ten pence a tin.
You can see it or buy it in Woolworth's
If Woolworth's have got any in.

IT'S GOT TO BE BETTER
THAN THE CUSTARD WE
TRIED LAST WEEK

I WON'T GO
TO WOOLIES

I won't go to Woolies
Any more-more-more
There's a big fat copper
On the door-door-door.
He grabs you by the collar
And makes you pay a dollar
I won't go to Woolies
Any more-more-more.

A SWING FOR SALE

A swing for sale
A monkey's tail
And if you take it
You go to gaol.

98

BARNEY HUGHES'S BREAD

Barney Hughes's bread
Sticks to your belly like lead
Not a bit of wonder
You rift like thunder
Barney Hughes's bread.

CHEWING GUM

P.K. chewing gum
8p a packet
First you suck it
Then you crack it
Then you stick it on your jacket
Then your Ma kicks up a racket.
P.K. chewing gum
8p a packet.

HALF-A-PINT OF PORTER

Half a pint of porter
Penny on the can
Hop there and back again
If you can.

LAY THE CLOTH

Lay the cloth, knife and fork
Bring me up a leg of pork
If it's lean bring it in
If it's fat take it back
Tell the man 'I don't want that.'

99

UP THE LADDER

Up the ladder
Down the wall
Half a loaf
To feed us all.
I'll buy milk
And you buy flour
There'll be pepper
In half an hour.

POTATOES

Yokie-cokie-yankie-yum
How do you like potatoes done?
Fried in brandy, fried in rum
That's how I like potatoes done.

CUPS AND SAUCERS

Cups and saucers
Ready for tea.
How many are we?
One-two-three.

KEEP IT BOILING

Keep it boiling
On the glimmer
If you don't
You'll miss your dinner.
North-East-South-West
Cadbury's chocolates are the best.

MOTHER

Mother
Mother
I am ill
Fetch the doctor from the hill.

Up the hill is much too far
You must buy a motor car.

Motor cars are much too dear
You must buy a pint of beer.

A pint of beer is much too strong
You must buy a treacle scone.

Treacle scones are much too tough
You must buy an ounce of snuff.

An ounce of snuff will make you sneeze
You must buy a pound of cheese.

Achoo!
Achoo!
Achoo!

I HAD THE
SCARLET FEVER

I had the scarlet fever
I had it very bad
And if you don't believe me
You can go and ask me dad.

IN DAYS OF OLD

In days of old, when knights were bold
And paper wasn't invented
They wiped themselves on telegraph poles
And walked away contented.

TIP AND TOE

Tip and toe
Breeze and blow
Turn the ship
And away we go.

ALL IN A ROW

All in a row
A bendy bow
Shoot a pigeon
Kill a crow
Shoot another
Kill his brother
Shoot again
Kill a wren
That will do for gentlemen.

THE LOOBY-LOOBY

Dance the looby-looby
Dance left and right
Dance the looby-looby
On Saturday night.

You put your left leg in
Your left leg out
You give it a shake
And turn it all about.

Oh, looby-looby-looby.

DOWN IN THE ALLEY

Down in the alley-o
Where we play relievi-o
Up comes her mother-o.
    'Have you seen my Mary-o?
    Why did you let her go?'
    'Because she bit my finger-o.'
    'Which finger did she bite?'
    'The little finger on the right.'

POPPETY-PIN

Dancety-diddlety-poppety-pin
Have a new dress when the summer comes in.
When summer goes south it's all worn out
Dancety-diddlety-poppety-pin.

NEW SHOES

New shoes new shoes
Red and pink and blue shoes
Tell me what you would choose
If you could buy some.

Buckle shoes bow shoes
Pretty pomty toe shoes
Strappy cappy low shoes
If you could try some.

Bright shoes white shoes
Dandy dance by night shoes
Perhaps a little tight shoes
Like some? So would I.

Flat shoes fat shoes
Stump along like that shoes
Wipe them on the mat shoes –
That's the sort they'll buy.

TAN

Dark tan
Light tan
Every tan
But tartan.

WHEN YOU ARE OLD

When you are old
And out of date
Remember corsets
Are £12.58.

HOUSE TO LET

House To Let
Apply Within.
Joan put out
For drinking gin.
Gin-gin-gin's
A very bad thing.
Joan goes out
And June comes in.

TWINKLE TWINKLE
CHOCOLATE BAR

Twinkle twinkle chocolate bar
Your dad drives a rusty car
Press the starter
Pull the choke
Off he goes in a cloud of smoke.

RACING CAR

Racing car
Number 9
Losing petrol
All the time
How many gallons did it lose?
One-two-three-four ...

PAPER HAT

I went out
And bought a paper hat
Bobby Copper grabbed it
And said, 'That's that.'
I asked him for it back.
He said he hadn't got it
'Hi, hi, curlywig
You've got it in your pocket.'

ARRESTED

He grabbed me by the collar
And tried to run me in
I closed my fist and knocked him stiff
And the boys began to sing:
    Ham and eggs for breakfast
    Ham and eggs for tea
    A loaf of bread as big as your head
    And stale as stale can be.

MURDER

Murder murder po-lis
Three flights up!
The woman with the middle door
Hit me with a cup.

My face is bleeding
My head is cut
Murder murder po-lis
Three flights up!

I WAS STANDING
ON THE CORNER

I was standing on the corner
Not doing any harm.
Along came a policeman
And took me by the arm.

He took me round the corner
And he rang a little bell.
Along came a police car
And took me to my cell.

I woke up in the morning
And looked up on the wall.
The cooties and the bedbugs
Were having a game of ball.

The score was six to nothing.
The bedbugs were ahead.
The cooties hit a homerun
And knocked me out of bed.

MONDAY TO THURSDAY

Monday night – Band of Hope.
Tuesday night – pull the rope.
Wednesday night – Pimlico.
Thursday evening – out you go.

WORLD WAR

World War One went crump
World War Two went clang
World War Three went thump
World War Four went BANG!

RAT–TAT–TAT

Rat-tat-tat
'Who is that?'
'Only grandma's pussy-cat.'
'What do you want?'
'A pint of milk.'
'Where's your money?'
'In my pocket.'
'Where's your pocket?'
'I forgot it.'

KNOCK ON THE KNOCKER

Knock on the knocker, ring on the bell.
Give us 50p for singing so well.
If you haven't 50p, 25 will do.
If you haven't 25, God bless you.

PROVERB

Apple crumble makes you rumble.
Apple tart makes you fart.

BANG–BANG–BANG

Bang-bang-bang
Eat brown bread
Ever seen a sausage
Fall down dead?
Out came a cabbage
Hit him on the head
Bang-bang-bang
Fall down dead.

SAUSAGES

I had a sausage
A pork-and-liver sausage
I put it in the oven for my tea-tea-tea.
I went down in the cellar
To get some salt and pepper
And the sausage ran after me-me-me.

★

The sausage is a cunning bird
With feathers long and wavy
It swims about in the frying pan
And lays its eggs in gravy.

BEANS

Baked Beans are good for your heart
The more you eat the more you fart
The more you fart the better you feel
Baked Beans with every meal!

GREEN PEAS

Green peas and mutton pies
Tell me where my lover lies
I'll be there before he dies
Green peas and mutton pies.

FARM FARE

Fodder in the loft
Poultry in the yard
Meat in the smokehouse
Barrels full of lard.

Milk in the dairy
Butter on the board
Coffee in the coffee tin
Sugar in the gourd.

PARDON ME
FOR BEING RUDE

Pardon me for being rude.
Don't blame me, blame my food.
There's a party down below –
One popped up to say hello.

DUMPLINGS

Hallelujah – make a dumpling
Hallelujah – make ten
Hallelujah – make a big one
Hallelujah – amen.

ALE

Round-about
Round-about
Maggoty pie
My dad likes ale
And so do I.

NEVSKI BRIDGE

On Nevski Bridge a Russian stood
Chewing his beard for lack of food.
Said he 'This stuff is tough to eat
But darn sight better than Shredded Wheat.'

IBBLE OBBLE

Ibble obble
Biggle bobble
Ibble obble out –
Turn the dirty dish-cloth
Turn it in and out.
Ibble obble
Biggle bobble
Ibble obble out.

EYES NOSE
MOUTH AND CHIN

Eyes nose mouth and chin
Walking down to Uncle Jim.
Uncle Jim makes lemonade
Round the corner chocolate's made.

SOLOMON AND SALOME

Solomon said to Salome
'We'll have no dancing here.'
'Nuts to you!' Salome said
And kicked the chandelier.

BELZEBUB

Here I come
Belzebub
Over my shoulders
I carry my club
In my hand
A dripping pan
Aren't I
A jolly old man.

MOSES

Moses was a holy man
Children had he seven
Moses hired a donkey cart
To drive them up to Heaven.
On his road he lost his way
Though he knew it well
Overturned his donkey cart
And landed up in Hell.

★

Moses supposes his toeses are roses
But Moses supposes erroneously
For nobody's toeses are posies of roses —
How could they possibly be?

NEBUCHADNEZZAR

A knife and a feather
Spells Nebuchadnezzar
A spoon and a fork
Spells Nebuchadnork
A new pair of slippers
And old pair of shoes
Spells Nebuchadnezzar
The King of the Jews.

HECTOR
PROTECTOR

Hector Protector
King of the Jews
Walk in my stockings
Step in my shoes.

GOOD KING
WENCESLAS

Good King Wenceslas
Knocked a bobby senseless
Right in the middle
Of Marks and Spencer's.

AS SHEPHERDS WATCHED
THEIR FLOCKS

As shepherds washed their socks by night
All seated round the tub
A bar of Sunlight soap flew out
And hit one in the mug.

★

As shepherds watched their flocks by night
While tuned to BBC
The angel of the Lord came down
And switched to ITV.

HE WANTS 'NEWS AT TEN'
SOMETHING'S HAPPENING
TONIGHT!

OLD KING COLE
AND FARMER WHITE

Old King Cole was a merry old soul
A merry old soul was he.
He called for a light in the middle of the night
To go to the WC.

The WC was occupied
And so was the bathroom sink.
But it had to be done
Oh it had to be done
So out of the window it went.

Now Farmer White was walking by
And heard a rumble in the sky
So he looked up as it came down
And now they call him Farmer Brown.

ROBINSON CRUSOE

Robinson Crusoe
Give us a call
Give us an answer
Or go to the wall.

GIPSY IN
THE MOONLIGHT

Gipsy in the moonlight
Gipsy in the dew
Gipsy never came back
Before the clock struck two.

Walk in Gipsy
Walk right in I say
Walk into my parlour
To hear my banjo play.

I love nobody
And nobody loves me
All I want is Mary
To come and dance with me.

CAESAR
AND BRUTUS

Caesar ad erum
Brutus ad erat
Caesar sic in omnibus
Brutus in his hat.

COLUMBUS

Columbus
Columbus
Sailed the blue
In fourteen hundred and ninety-two.
Columbus
Columbus
Went to sea
And didn't get back till ninety-three.

OLIVER CROMWELL

Oliver Cromwell
Lost his shoe
At the battle of Waterloo.
Right turn –
Left turn –
Come to attention – toodle-oo!

GUY FAWKES

Guy Fawkes, Guy!
Hit him in the eye!
Hang him on a lamp-post
And leave him there to die!

QUEEN ANNE

Queen Anne
Queen Anne
Sitting in the sun
White as a lily
And brown as a bun.
She is in love
Wearing a glove –
First she takes it off
Then she puts it on.

ROBERT BURNS

Rabbie Burns was born in Ayr
Now he's in Trafalgar Square.
If you want tae see him there
Jump on a bus and skip the fare.

WALLACE BEARY

One-two-three-a-leary
I spy Wallace Beary
Sitting on his bum-ba-reary
Eating chocolate biscuits.

KAISER BILL

Kaiser Bill went up the hill
To see the British army.
General French jumped out of a trench
And made the cows go barmy.

★

Cuff the Kaiser
Cuff the cat
King George never
Did a thing like that.

MISTER HITLER

Mister Hitler
I've been thinking
What on earth
Have you been drinking?
Smells like whisky
Tastes like wine
O my God
It's iodine!

HARK THE HERALD
ANGELS SING

Hark! the Herald angels sing
Mrs Simpson's pinched our king.
Took him for a country walk
And left us with the Duke of York.

BURKE AND HARE

Burke and Hare
What a pair!
Killed a girl
And didn't care.

Then they put her
In a box
And sent it round
To Doctor Knox.

DIANA DORS

I'm Diana Dors
I'm a movie star
I've a cute-cute figure
And a motor car.

I've got the hips
The legs and the lips
I'm Diana Dors
I'm a movie star.

CHARLIE CHAPLIN

Charlie Chaplin
Sat on a pin.
How many inches
Did it go in?
One for 'Ow!'
Half for 'Ou!'
Half a half for Timbuctoo.

FINIGAN

This old man his name was Finigan
He had hairs upon his chinigan
Along came the wind and blew them inigan
Poor old Michael Finigan – beginigan.

RINGO

Ringo-Ringo-Ringo Starr
Locked his tonsils in a jar
When they opened it for air
All they heard was 'Yeh-yeh-yeh.'

YANKEE DOODLE

Yankee Doodle went to town
To buy himself a pony.
Stuck a feather in his hat
And called him macaroni.

MISS MUFFET

Little Miss Muffet
Sat on a tuffet
Eating some Irish stew.
Down came a spider
That sat down beside her
And so she ate him, too.

OLIVER TWIST

Oliver-Oliver-Oliver Twist
Bet you a penny you can't do this:
Number one – touch your tongue
Number two – touch your shoe
Number three – touch your knee
Number four – touch the floor
Number five – stay alive
Number six – wiggle your hips
Number seven – jump to Heaven
Number eight – bang the gate
Number nine – walk the line
Number ten – start again.

POPEYE

I'm Popeye the sailor man
I live in a caravan
I like to go swimmin'
With bare naked women
I'm Popeye the sailor man.

TEMPTATION

Temptation!
Temptation!
Temptation!
Dick Barton went down to the station.
Blondie was there
All naked and bare
Temptation!
Temptation!
Temptation!

TARZAN

Tarzan Tarzan in the air
Tarzan lost his underwear.

Tarzan say 'Me no care
Jane make me another pair.'

Jane Jane in the air
Jane has lost her underwear.

Jane she say 'Me no care
Cheetah make me another pair.'

Cheetah Cheetah in the air
Cheetah lost his underwear.

Cheetah say 'Me no care
Cheetah need no underwear.'

TARZAN AND JANE

Snakes in the grass go hiss–hiss–hiss
Tarzan and Jane go kiss–kiss–kiss.

DAVY CROCKETT

Born on a table top in Joe's Café
Dirtiest place in the USA
Shot his father when he was three
Polished off his mother with DDT.
Davy
Davy Crockett
King of the Wild Frontier.

SLINKY–MALINKY

Slinky-Malinky long legs
With umbrella feet
Went into the pictures
And fell through the seat.

HEIGH–HO!

Heigh-ho!
Heigh-ho!
I bit the teacher's toe
She bit mine too
And turned it blue
Heigh-ho!
Heigh-ho!

Heigh-ho!
Heigh-ho!
It's out to play we go
With hand grenades
And cannonades
Heigh-ho!
Heigh-ho!

BETTER NOT SAY IT

Better not say it
His mother will faint
And his father will fall
In a bucket of paint.

NO LIP —
POTATO CHIP

No lip – potato chip
Shut up – ketchup
Your fault – garlic salt
Tell lies – bubble eyes.

KNOCK-KNEED CHICKEN

I'm a knock-kneed chicken
I'm a bow-legged sparrow
Missed my bus so I went by barrow
Went to the café for my dinner and my tea
Too many radishes –
Pardon me.

SNAP

Thanks for the photo
It really was nice
I put it in the attic
To scare away the mice.

CHANTS

Hold a feather in frosty weather
When the wind blows we go together.

★

Boiled beans and melted butter
Ladies and gentlemen come to supper.

★

Daily Mirror and Evening News
Ever seen a parrot wearing shoes?

★

They're going to build a house.
    BOO!
A public house.
    HOORAY!
There'll only be one bar.
    BOO!
A mile long.
    HOORAY!
There'll only be one barmaid.
    BOO!
For each customer.
    HOORAY!
They're going to water the beer.
    BOO!
With whiskey.
    HOORAY!
They're going to close at ten.
    BOO!
In the morning.
    HOORAY!

Ten in the bed
One gave a shout
'Everyone turn!
And one fell out.

Nine in the bed
One gave a shout
'Everyone turn!
And another fell out.

[And so on. Then:]

One in the bed
One gave a gasp
'Alone, alone,
Alone at last!

★

Eggs and bacon, chips and cheese
What can I have for dinner please?

SAME TO YOU

Same to you with knobs on
Cabbages with clogs on
Elephants with slippers on
You with dirty knickers on.

DANNY

Danny
Danny
Don't be blue
Frankenstein was ugly too.

HOLLYWOOD

If you can't go to Hollywood
You don't have to cry
Paul Newman is handsome
But so am I.

MAD

Mad–mad–mad
Just like your poor old dad
You live in a tent
And pay no rent –
Mad–mad–mad.

GOD

God made mountains
God made lakes
God made you
We all make mistakes.

YOUR FACE AND MINE

Roses are red
Cabbages are green
My face may be funny
But yours is a scream.

THERE SHE GOES

There she goes
There she goes
Six-inch heels
And pointed toes.
See her feet
Thinks she's neat
Holes in her stockings
And dirty feet.

133

DREAMT I DIED

Dreamt I died
And left my bed.
'Where are you from?' St Peter said.
I said 'Birmingham.'
'I declare,' St Peter said
'You're the first from there.'

THE GIRLS IN SPAIN

The girls in Spain
Wash their knickers in champagne
And the way they shake
Is enough to kill a snake
And when the snake is dead
They make handbags from its head
And when the bag is full
They wrap it up in wool
And when the wool is worn
They take it home to darn
And they darn it with wire
They throw it on the fire
O Oochy-Koochy-Koochy!
That's what it's all about.

TIDDLY WINKS

Tiddly Winks old man
Suck a lemon if you can
If you can't suck a lemon
Suck an old tin can.

ARE YOU THE GUY

Are you the guy
That told the guy
That I'm the guy
That gave the guy
One in the eye?

TIT FOR TAT

Tit for tat
Butter for fat
Kill my dog
I'll kill your cat.

DIE DOG DIE

Die dog die
In your grandmother's eye
Getting worse
Getting worse
Put a penny in your purse
Die dog die.

WHAT'S YOUR NAME?

'What's your name?'
'Charlie Brown.'
'Pardon me while I knock you down.'

SHUT UP

Shut up
Button your lip
Cork your eye
With a juniper pip!

CRY–BABY–CRY

Cry-baby-cry
Punch him in the eye
Tie him to a lamp-post
And leave him there to die.

TELL–TALE–TIT

Tell-tale-tit
Your tongue will be split
And all the little birds
Will have a little bit

COWARDY–CUSTARD

Cowardy cowardy custard
Can't eat bread and mustard
Burned his tongue and home did run
Cowardy-cowardy-custard.

MIND YOUR OWN BEESWAX

Mind your own beeswax
Cook your own fish
Don't let your nose drip
In my dish.

SEE MY FINGER?

See my finger?
See my thumb?
See my fist?
Run! Run! Run!

TOODLE-DOODLE-OODLE-OO

Toodle-doodle-oodle-oo
They need monkeys in the zoo
I'd apply if I were you
And get the situation ...

137

NO RETURNS

A pinch and a punch
The first of a bunch –
And no returns.

A push and a kick
For being too quick –
And no returns.

A boot and a blow
For being so slow –
And no returns.

A slap in the eye
For being so sly –
And no returns.

This knock is the last
Because I am so fast –
And no returns.

BANG BANG

Bang bang
You're dead
Fifty bullets in your head.

★

Bang bang
Pop pop
You're dead
I'm not.

DAFTIE AND BARMY

Daftie and Barmy
Go and join the army
Get knocked out
With a Brussels sprout –
Daftie and Barmy.

SHAKE HANDS BROTHER

Shake hands brother
You're a rogue
And I'm another.
You stole meat
I stole bone
You'll go to Hell
And I'll go home.

PRAYER

Holy Mary Mother of God
Pray for me and Tommy Todd.
I'm a Cat. and he's a Prod.
Holy Mary Mother of God.

ROMAN SOLDIERS

We will have a war with you
We will have a war with you
We will have a war with you
We are Roman Soldiers.

Bang! Bang! Bang!

Now we've only got one leg
Now we've only got one leg
Now we've only got one leg
We are Roman Soldiers.

Bang! Bang! Bang!

Now we've only got one eye
Now we've only got one eye
Now we've only got one eye
We are Roman Soldiers.

Bang! Bang! Bang!

Now we've only got one arm
Now we've only got one arm
Now we've only got one arm
We are Roman Soldiers.

Bang! Bang! Bang!

Now we're dead and in our graves
Now we're dead and in our graves
Now we're dead and in our graves
We are Roman Soldiers.

Bang! Bang! Bang!

Now we are alive again
Now we are alive again
Now we are alive again
We are Roman Soldiers.

Bang! Bang! Bang!

DIAMONDS

Diamonds shine
Diamonds glisten
You can talk
But I won't listen.

THE MOLE

The mole, the mole
He lives in a hole
As blind as a bat
And doesn't give a rap.

INCY WINCY SPIDER

Incy Wincy spider
Climbed the water spout
Down came the rain
And washed poor Incy out.
Out came the sun
And dried up the rain
Incy Wincy spider
Climbed the spout again.

THE BUMBLEBEE

The bumblebee
Sits on the wall
And says 'I hum.'
And that is all.

OOEY GOOEY

Ooey Gooey was a worm
A little worm was he
He sat upon the railway track
The train he did not see.
OOEY GOOEY!

THE FLEA AND THE FLY

A flea met a fly in a flue.
Said the flea 'Let us fly.'
Said the fly 'Let us flee.'
So they flew through a flaw in the flue.

THE BUG
AND THE FLEA

A bug and a flea
Went to sea
On a reel of cotton.
The bug was drowned
The flea was found
Stuck to a mermaid's bottom.

BAT

Cheese and bread
For the bat-bat-bat
Come into
My hat-hat-hat.

FUZZY-WUZZY

Fuzzy-Wuzzy was a bear
Fuzzy-Wuzzy had no hair
So Fuzzy-Wuzzy wasn't fuzzy, wuzzy?

THE WORM

I saw a little worm
Wriggling on its belly.
I watched it for a while
Then squashed it with my wellie.

QUICK

Quick! Quick!
The cat's been sick.

Where? Where?
Under the chair.

Hasten! Hasten!
Fetch a basin.

Too late. Too late.
The carpet's in an awful state.

Alas! Alas! All in vain.
The cat has licked it up again.

THE BLACK CAT

The black cat piddled in the white cat's eye
The white cat said 'Cor Blimey!'
'I'm sorry, mate, to piddle in your eye
But I didn't see you behind me.'

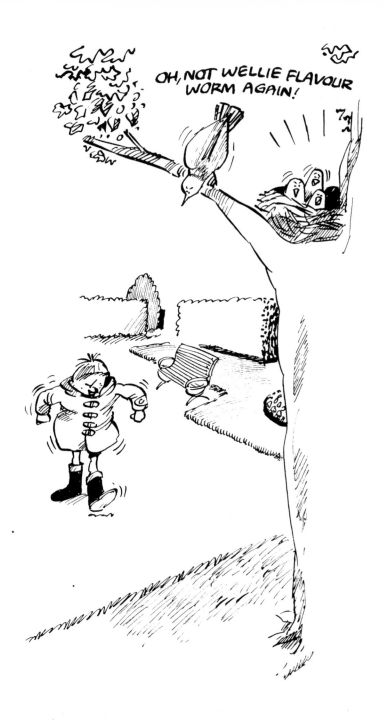

OUR OLD DOG

Our old dog
He don't mind
He'll eat your dinner
Then bite your behind.

THE LITTLE PIG

The lightning flashed
The thunder roared
Heaven and earth were shaken
The little pig
Curled his tail
And ran to save his bacon.

WILLIAM'S PIG

William had a pretty pig
Not too little and not too big.
When it was alive it lived in clover
But now it's dead and that's all over.

JACK PURVES' MARE

Tomorrow's the fair!
We'll all be there
To see Jack Purves' lily-white mare.
There'll be silver ships with painted sails
And wooden horses with hairy tails.

THE DONKEY

Matthew Mark Luke and John
Hold the donkey till I get on.
If he kicks pull his tail
If he widdles hold the pail.

INKY–PINKY–PONKY

Inky-pinky-ponky
Daddy bought a donkey.
The donkey died
And daddy cried
'Inky-pinky-ponky.'

RED WHITE AND BLUE

Red white and blue
The dirty kangaroo
Went behind the lamp-post
And did his number two.

THE ELEPHANT

The elephant's a pretty bird
It flits from bough to bough
It builds its nest in a rhubarb tree
And whistles like a cow.

MARY AND HER LAMB

Mary had a little lamb
It was a greedy glutton
She gave it ice-cream every day
And now it's frozen mutton.

★

Mary had a little lamb
Her father shot it dead
And so it went to school with her
Between two bits of bread.

★

Mary had a little lamb
It drank her castor oil
And everywhere it went that day
It fertilized the soil.

★

Mary had a little lamb
She fed it bacon rind
I often saw her lamb before
But never her behind.

WAY DOWN SOUTH

Way down south where the ripe bananas grow
An ant stepped on an elephant's toe.
The elephant cried with tears in his eyes
'Pick on somebody your own size.'

THE GARDEN

I was in the garden
Picking beans and peas
I dropped them from laughing
When I heard a chicken sneeze.

MITTY–MATTY

Mitty-Matty had a hen
She laid eggs for gentlemen
Gentlemen come once a day
Mitty-Matty runs away.
  Jumble-jimble
  Who's at home?
  Mum and Dad and Jumping Joan.

THE SWAN

The swan swam over the sea
Swim
Swan
Swim
The swan swam back again
Swim
Swim
Swan.

CUCKOO

Cuckoo cuckoo
Cherry tree
Catch a bird
And give it me.

★

Cuckoo
Cuckoo
Cherry tree
Lay an egg
And give it me.
Lay another
For my brother.

CROW

Crow
Crow
Get out of my sight
Or I'll kill your father and mother tonight.

UNDER THE APPLE TREE

As I sat under the apple tree
A birdie sent his love to me
And as I wiped it from my eye
I said 'Thank goodness cows can't fly.'

BLUEBELLS
MY COCKLESHELLS

Bluebells my cockleshells
Farewell my mother
Bury me in the old churchyard
Beside my eldest brother.
My coffin shall be white
With six white angels by my side.
Two to watch and two to pray
And two to carry my soul away.

BURYING

When you die
They cover you up in a clean white sheet
And bury you down a hundred feet
Your blood it goes a horrible green
And your bones they turn to Cornish cream.
The worms go in
The worms come out
They go in thin
And they come out stout.

REMEMBER

Remember M
Remember E
Put them together
Remember ME.

Acknowledgements

The rhymes in this book came from the memories of my friends, acquaintances, several correspondents, and a number of West London schoolchildren; from magazines, learned journals, and pamphlets; and from other books. Among the Books Consulted, those by Iona and Peter Opie are indispensable to anyone compiling an anthology of this kind; I think it unlikely that their *Lore and Language of Schoolchildren* will be superceded for many years. Thereafter, I would like to give particular thanks to Mrs Susan E. Bates, Headmistress, Barlby Primary School, London; Miss Eleri Jones of Radio Club, Radio 4, the BBC; Mrs E.K. Nichols, Head of The Upper School, Beaverwood School for Girls, Bromley; Miss Pauline Page, Librarian, Lornskill Academy, Alloa, Clackmannanshire; Mrs Sonia Pollock, Headmistress, Oxford Gardens Primary School and Mr Michael Woolman, Headmaster, Fox's School, both in London. May I also thank the staff of the Reference Library, the Royal Borough of Kensington and Chelsea; the staff of the Reading Room, Department of Printed Books, the British Library; the staff of the Library, the British Folklore Society, University College, London; the staff of the London Library; and Mr Timothy Auger, Miss Anabel Bartlett, Miss Janet Bentley of Fox's School, Mrs Treld Bicknell, Mr Peter Bonnici, Miss Pauline Briers, Miss Mary E. Bryan, Mr Michael Chassay, Margaret N. Coughlan of the Library of Congress, Washington DC, Miss Nell Dunn, Miss Victoria Eldon, Lord Peregrine Eliot, Mrs Helen Elliott, Mr Derek Farmer, Miss E. Frances, Miss Marjorie L. Furner, Mrs Laura Gascoigne, Miss Rosemary Gleeson of Trinity College Library, Dublin, Mr Charles Graham, Miss Margaret Hare, Miss Patricia Harris, Mr Michael Hastings, Miss Anne Head, Miss Joanne Head, Rosemary Hill of *Country Life*, Mrs M. Holliday, Miss Libby Houston, Jean Huse of the English Speaking Union, Mr Richard Ingrams, Mr Brian Jenkins of the Cambridge University Library, Mr T. Vaughan Jones of the Welsh Folk Museum, Miss Mary Kenny, Miss Robin Lambert, Miss Elaine Lever, Miss Eileen Lewis, Miss Bridget Loney, Mr Michael Longley, Dr Emily Lyle of the School of Scottish Studies, Mr D. Mackay of Burton End School, Suffolk, Miss Gerda Mayer, Miss Joan Nevin, Mr Don Patter, Miss Margaret Payne of the National Book League, Mr Barney Platts-Mills, Mr Craig Raine, Mr Graham Reeves, Miss Susan Richards, Mr Scott Roberts, Miss Patricia Rowan of the *Times Educational Supplement*, Mrs Margaret Spencer, Miss Anne Stevenson, Mr Bernard Stone, Mr B.E. Strickland, Mrs Georgina Warrilow of the Bodleian Library, Mr Paul White, Mrs D.J. Wight, Mr Heathcote Williams, Mr P.E. Wood, Mr Archibald Young, and Miss Caroline Younger.

Books and publications consulted

Abrahams, R.D., *Jump-Rope Rhymes* (1969) — and Rankin, L., *Counting-Out Rhymes* (1980)

Bett, Henry, *The Games of Children* (1929)

Bolton, Henry Carrington, *The Counting-Out Rhymes of Children* (1888)

Bonser, William, *A Bibliography of 'Folklore'* (1961)

Brady, Eilis, *All In! All In!* (1975)

Chambers, Robert, *Popular Rhymes of Scotland* (1869)

Coffin, Tristram P., *Analytical Index to Volumes 1-70 of the American Folklore Society* (1958)

Colgan, Brendan, *Let's Play* (1980)

Crossing, W., *Folk Rhymes of Devon* (1911)

The Cumnock Academy, *Bluebells My Cockle Shells* (1961)

Daiken, Leslie Herbert, *Out Goes She* (1963)

Douglas, Norman, *London Street Games* (1916)

Elder, Jacob D., *Song Games from Trinidad and Tobago* (1965)

Evans, Patricia, *Jump Rope Rhymes* (1954)

Factor, June, *Far Out, Brussel Sprout* (1983)

Folklore (1890-   )

Ford, Robert, *Children's Rhymes, Children's Games — Children's Songs, Children's Stories* (1904)

Fowke, Edith, *Sally Go Round the Sun* (1969)

Fraser, Amy Stewart, *Dae Ye Min' Langsyne* (1975)

Gomme, Lady Alice Bertha, *Traditional Games of England, Scotland and Ireland* (1894)

Gullen, F. Doreen, *Traditional Rhymes and Number Games* Publications of the Scottish Council for Research in Education No. 32 (1950)

Halliwell, James Orchard, *Popular Rhymes and Nursery Tales* (1849)

Hanley, Clifford, *Dancing in the Streets* (1958)

Higham, J.A., *Rhymes from the Schoolyard* (1983)

Humphreys, Jennett, *Old Welsh Knee Songs, Frolic and Passtime Verse* (1894)

Jones, Daniel Parry, *Welsh Children's Games and Passtimes* (1961)

Journal of the American Folklore Society (1888-   )

Knapp, Mary and Herbert, *One Potato* (1976)

MacBain, J. Murray, *The London Treasury of Nursery Rhymes* (n.d.)

Montgomerie, Nora and William, *The Hogarth Book of Scottish Nursery Rhymes* (1946) — *Sandy Candy* (1948)

Munsterberg, Peggy, *The Penguin Book of Bird Poetry* (1984)

New Society (9.2.1978 and 2.6.1983)

Northall, G.F., *English Folk Rhymes* (1892)

O'Hare, Colette, *What Do You Feed Your Donkey On?* (1978)

Opie, Iona and Peter, *I Saw Esau* (1947) — *The Oxford Dictionary of Nursery Rhymes* (1952) — *The Lore and Language of Schoolchildren* (1959) — *Children's Games in Street and Playground* (1969)

Page, Pauline, *The Story of Valentines: Valentine Verses Collected from the Bannockburn High School and the Lornshill Academy* (1984)

Pierce, Maggi Kerr, *Keep the Kettle Boiling* (1983)

Ritchie, James, *The Singing Street* (1965) — *Golden City* (1965)

Rutherford, Frank, *All the Way to Pennywell* (1971)

Shaw, Frank, *You Know Me Aunty Nelly* (1969)

Stone, Danielle, *Claps, Skips, Dips, Barlby Road School* (1983)

Sutton-Smith, Brian, *The Games of New Zealand Children* (1959) — *The Folkgames of Children* (1972)

The Times Literary Supplement (14.7.1978)

Turner, Ian, *Cinderella Dressed in Yella* (1969)

Udal, Arthur Uredale, *Dorsetshire Folk-lore* (1922)

Uttley, Allison, *Country Hoard* (1943)

Vansittart, Peter, *Voices from the Great War* (1981)

Whithers, Carl, *A Rocket in my Pocket* (1948)

Williams-Ellis, Clough, *In and Out of Doors* (1937)

Wood, Ray, *Fun in American Folk Rhymes* (1952)

Index of First Lines

159